Adapted from *The Nutcracker and the Mouse King* by E.T.A. Hoffmann
Retold by Hannah Pang
Illustrated by Federica Frenna

STUDIO
PRESS

© 2018 Studio Press

Edited by Frankie Jones • Designed by Claire Munday

Printed and bound in China, 0240718
2 4 6 8 10 9 7 5 3 1

Studio Press
An imprint of Kings Road Publishing
Part of Bonnier Publishing
The Plaza, 535 King's Road,
London, SW10 0SZ
www.studiopressbooks.co.uk
www.bonnierpublishing.co.uk

The Nutcracker
and the
Mouse King

A Search & Find Book

Illustrated by Federica Frenna
Original story by E.T.A. Hoffmann • Retold by Hannah Pang

E.T.A. Hoffmann
1776 – 1822

Ernst Theodor Amadeus Hoffmann was a German writer of fantasy and horror, as well as a composer, a music critic and talented artist. At birth he was given the name "Ernst Theodor Wilhelm Hoffmann", but later changed this in honour of the composer Wolfgang Amadeus Mozart.

Hoffmann studied the theory of law and went on to become a Prussian law officer in 1800, serving until 1806. Hoffmann's enthusiasm for music remained, and he held several positions as a conductor, critic and theatrical musical director until 1814. After this, he was appointed to the court of appeal in Berlin, becoming councillor in 1816. It was during this time that his opera, *Undine*, was performed by the Berlin Theatre.

However, it is for his stories that Hoffmann is most remembered. The unusual themes and techniques used by Hoffmann were to inspire many other writers who followed in his footsteps, including Charles Dickens and C.S. Lewis – such as sending child characters to magical lands through the gateways of everyday objects. Hoffmann even inspired a French composer called Jacques Offenbach to base an opera, *Les Contes d'Hoffmann* (*The Tales of Hoffmann*), on him and three of his works.

Hoffmann's final novel is considered a masterpiece, as well as the strangest novel of the 19th century. *The Life and Opinions of the Tomcat Murr* is about two fictional texts that accidentally get merged into one at the printers: the autobiography of a tomcat called Murr and a biography about a genius musician, Johannes Kreisler. Sadly, the project was left unfinished due to Hoffmann's death in 1822. He is buried in a cemetery in Berlin.

The Nutcracker and the Mouse King
1816

When most people think of *The Nutcracker*, they often think of the ballet. In fact, the original tale – *The Nutcracker and the Mouse King* – is much longer than the ballet version and has a story (*The Tale of the Hard Nut*) within a story. The German original was first published in 1816 in a volume entitled *Kinder-Märchen* (*Children's Stories*). It was later republished in the first volume of Hoffmann's own four-volume collection, *Die Serapionsbrüder* (*The Serapion Brethren*) (1819-1821).

The Nutcracker and the Mouse King is rarely translated in its entirety. It was adapted in 1845 by Alexandre Dumas, the French writer who also wrote *The Three Musketeers*. He entitled the adaptation *Histoire d'un Casse-Noisette* (*The History of a Nutcracker*) and removed some of the darker, scarier parts of the story. In 1892 Dumas' version was converted into a ballet, which premiered at the Mariinsky Theatre in Saint Petersburg, Russia. Russian composer Pyotr Ilyich Tchaikovsky created the unforgettable music for this – including "The Dance of the Sugar Plum Fairy" – which many of us will be familiar with today.

The ballet is now performed all around the world, especially at Christmastime. It's not difficult to see why such a tale – complete with magical toys that spring to life and a heavenly land of sweets – has captured the imaginations of so many and will continue to do so for many years to come.

Meet the Characters

There is a festive and fascinating world of characters waiting to be discovered on the search and find pages, from Marie and her family to the mysterious Godpapa Drosselmeier, the brave Nutcracker and the wicked Mouse King.

MARIE STAHLBAUM

FRITZ STAHLBAUM

LOUISE STAHLBAUM

"Godpapa Drosselmeier was anything but a nice-looking man. He was little and lean, with a great many wrinkles on his face, a big patch of black plaister where his right eye ought to have been, and not a hair on his head; which was why he wore a fine white wig, made of glass."

MARIE'S FATHER

MARIE'S MOTHER

GODPAPA DROSSELMEIER

THE NUTCRACKER

THE MOUSE KING

"As Marie kept looking at this little man, whom she had quite fallen in love with at first sight, she saw more and more clearly what a sweet nature and disposition was legible in his countenance."

DROSSELMEIER'S NEPHEW

THE PRINCESS

DAME MOUSEYRINKS
QUEEN OF THE MICE

Christmas Eve

During which…

The drawing room is being decorated,
Marie and Fritz wait in the parlour,
Fritz has seen Godpapa Drosselmeier,
They wonder what he's made for them,
A gleam of light flashes upon the wall,
A silver bell rings kling-ling,
The doors fly wide open, and
Papa and Mamma lead them out.

Search and find:

AN EXCITED MARIE

A CURIOUS FRITZ

A KIND PAPA

A LOVING MAMMA

A SILVER BELL

A PORTRAIT OF GODPAPA

A SLEEPING CAT

A BLUE JUG

A CLOCK SAYING HALF PAST SEVEN

A SWEET DOLL

The Great Christmas Tree

Beneath which…

The two children stand speechless,
Presents are piled under a Christmas tree,
Marie receives a silk dress with ribbons,
Fritz receives a toy fox and soldiers,
Godpapa Drosselmeier reveals his gift,
It's a magnificent clockwork castle:
The children quickly become bored and
Godpapa Drosselmeier puts it in a box.

Search and find:

*A DISAPPOINTED
GODPAPA*

*A DISTRACTED
FRITZ*

*A THANKFUL
MARIE*

A BOWL OF FRUIT

A DOLL

*SIX PICTURE
BOOKS*

*MARIE'S
SILK DRESS*

*FRITZ'S
TOY FOX*

*EIGHT SOLDIERS
ON HORSEBACK*

*THE CLOCKWORK
CASTLE*

The Nutcracker

In which…

Marie discovers the Nutcracker,
She falls in love with him at first sight,
Papa says he belongs to all the children,
He shows them how to crack a nut,
Fritz breaks the Nutcracker's jaw,
Marie cries bitterly,
She binds the wounded Nutcracker and
Wraps him in a handkerchief.

Search and find:

*A SAD
MARIE*

*A WOUNDED
NUTCRACKER*

*A NAUGHTY
FRITZ*

*AN OBSERVING
LOUISE*

*A CLOCKWORK
CASTLE*

*A ROCKING
HORSE*

*A PILE
OF NUTS*

*FIVE
MICE*

*FOUR CANDLESTICK
HOLDERS*

A CLOCK

The Glass Cupboard

In which…

Marie and Fritz are playing with toys,
Mamma asks them to go to bed,
Marie begs to stay up longer,
She tells the Nutcracker he'll be fixed,
Thousands of eyes shine in the dark,
A mouse army gallops into the room,
The Mouse King rises through the floor,
And Marie falls and breaks the cupboard.

Search and find:

*A TIRED
FRITZ*

*A TOY
LION*

*A TINY
PRINCESS*

*A MOUSE
HOLE*

*A SLEEPY
NUTCRACKER*

*TWO MAGICAL
GODPAPAS*

*THE RISING
MOUSE KING*

*A CLOCK
SHOWING MIDNIGHT*

*A FLORAL
SOFA*

*A COLOURFUL
MERRY-GO-
ROUND*

The Battle

In which…

The Nutcracker leaps from the cupboard,
Fritz's army of toy soldiers join him,
They battle against the mouse army,
It's difficult to see who might win,
The Nutcracker's army retreats,
The Mouse King seizes the Nutcracker,
Marie throws a shoe at the king and
The pain in her arm causes her to faint.

Search and find:

*A BRAVE
NUTCRACKER*

*A DESPAIRING
MARIE*

*AN EVIL
MOUSE KING*

A DRUMMER

A GUIDON

THE ARTILLERY

*TWO SCARED
DOLLS*

*MARIE'S
SHOE*

*TWO CHINESE
EMPERORS*

*A FIERCE
LION*

The Patient

In which…

Marie awakens from a deep sleep,
Dr Wendelstern is by her side,
Marie tells Mamma about the battle,
Mamma says to stop talking nonsense,
Marie must stay in bed for a few days,
Godpapa Drosselmeier pays her a visit,
He has fixed the Nutcracker and
Tells them all a story about him…

Search and find:

*A WOUNDED
MARIE*

*A MEDICINE
BAG*

*A GLASS OF
WATER*

*A PAIR
OF SHOES*

*A BOTTLE
OF MEDICINE*

*A CONCERNED
GODPAPA*

*A LISTENING
FRITZ*

MARIE'S DOLL

*A REPAIRED
NUTCRACKER*

*A PURPLE
TEACUP*

Godpapa's Story: An Angry King

In which…

Godpapa Drosselmeier begins his story:
There was a mouse, Dame Mouseyrinks,
Her family ate all of the king's sausages,
The king sentenced the mice to death,
He asked a clockmaker to set some traps,
Dame Mouseyrinks managed to escape,
She threatened the princess and so
The princess was guarded by cats at night.

Search and find:

*AN EVIL DAME
MOUSEYRINKS*

*SIX HUNGRY
MICE*

*A KIND
QUEEN*

*A CROSS
KING*

*A BUSY
CLOCKMAKER*

*A STRING
OF SAUSAGES*

*NINE
MOUSE TRAPS*

*A SWEET
PRINCESS*

*TEN
CATS*

*A GOLD
THRONE*

Godpapa's Story: The Crackatook

In which…

Dame Mouseyrinks bit the princess,
The princess became quite ugly,
Her parents were devastated,
The king blamed the clockmaker,
He asked him to change her back,
A Crackatook nut was the only cure,
It had to be cracked by a special man and
The clockmaker was ordered to find both.

Search and find:

A BITING DAME
MOUSEYRINKS

A SLEEPING
PRINCESS

A SAD
QUEEN

A DEVASTATED
KING

A HORRIFIED
NURSE

AN ACCUSED
CLOCKMAKER

A CLOCK
SHOWING MIDNIGHT

A CRACKED
FLOORBOARD

A FULL
MOON

AN EMPTY
MOUSE TRAP

Godpapa's Story: The Revenge

In which…

The clockmaker found the Crackatook nut,
It belonged to his cousin in Nuremberg,
His cousin had a son,
The son cracked the nut for the princess,
She became beautiful again,
The son stepped on Dame Mouseyrinks,
Who turned him into the Nutcracker and
Said the Mouse King would get revenge.

Search and find:

*A HAPPY
CLOCKMAKER*

*A CRACKATOOK
NUT*

*A GENEROUS
COUSIN*

*A HELPFUL
SON*

*A BEAUTIFUL
PRINCESS*

*AN ANGRY
DAME MOUSEYRINKS*

*FIVE
SPINNING TOPS*

*A FARAWAY
CASTLE*

*A WOODEN
TRAIN SET*

*AN ABANDONED
PUPPET*

Time for Tea

At which…

Marie finds the Nutcracker,
He lies still and motionless,
The family sit at the tea table,
Marie talks of the battle again,
Mamma says she dreamed it,
Marie questions her godpapa,
Why won't he help the Nutcracker?
He says only she can help.

Search and find:

A WELL
MARIE

A LIFELESS
NUTCRACKER

A JAR OF
JAM

EIGHT
BISCUITS

A LISTENING
GODPAPA

A SIPPING
PAPA

SIX
TEACUPS

SIX
TEASPOONS

TWO SLEEPING
DOLLS

A GOLDEN
OWL

Victory

In which…

The Mouse King enters Marie's room,
He threatens to chew up the Nutcracker,
Marie doesn't know what to do,
The Nutcracker comes alive,
He asks Marie for a sword,
He leaves and comes back transformed,
He's defeated the Mouse King, and
Asks Marie to follow him…

Search and find:

*A GREEDY
MOUSE KING*

*A SCARED
MARIE*

*EIGHT NIBBLED
CAKES*

*EIGHT NIBBLED
GINGERBREAD MEN*

*A CRACK IN
THE WALL*

*A BRAVE
NUTCRACKER*

*A TOY
SWORD*

*TWO
SHOES*

*A COIN
PURSE*

*MARIE'S
DOLL*

The Land of Sweets

In which…

Marie follows the Nutcracker,
They go into the wardrobe,
They climb into Papa's coat,
It leads to a magical land,
They visit towns and villages,
The buildings are made of sweets,
The rivers run with lemonade and
They sail on Lake Rosa to the city.

Search and find:

A FOLLOWING MARIE

A LEADING NUTCRACKER

FIVE GRACEFUL SWANS

PAPA'S WINTER COAT

A SMALL LADDER

A SWEET GATE

SIX MONKEYS

A GOLD CHAIR

FIVE CHILDREN FISHING

A GINGERBREAD CHURCH

GINGERTHORPE

CANDY MEAD

CHRISTMAS WOOD

BONBONVILLE

The City

In which…

Marie and the Nutcracker visit the city,
The houses are made of sugar,
There are thousands of people,
They go to the Marzipan Castle,
The Nutcracker's sisters hold a banquet,
He tells them about the battle,
A mist rises around Marie and
She finds herself floating.

Search and find:

*A HAPPY
NUTCRACKER*

*A CURIOUS
MARIE*

*EIGHT
LITTLE BOYS*

*A MARZIPAN
CASTLE*

*TWO
DOLPHINS*

*TWO SILVER
SOLDIERS*

*A LARGE
CAKE*

*THREE
FOUNTAINS*

*A MONKEY STEALING
A CUPCAKE*

*THREE FLYING
PARROTS*

Happily Ever After

In which…

Marie wakes to see Mamma,
Mamma says she's been dreaming again,
Marie holds the Mouse King's crown,
Papa calls her a liar,
Marie tells the Nutcracker he's not ugly,
There's a loud bang,
He turns back into a real prince and
Asks Marie to live in Marzipan Castle.

Search and find:

A TRANSFORMED PRINCE

A HAPPY GODPAPA

A LIFELESS NUTCRACKER

A BOWL OF NUTS

THE MOUSE KING'S CROWN

THREE MICE

FOUR RED TOY SOLDIERS

A SLEEPING CAT

A CLOCK SHOWING THREE O'CLOCK

A GOLDEN COACH

CHRISTMAS EVE

THE GREAT CHRISTMAS TREE

THE NUTCRACKER

THE GLASS CUPBOARD

GODPAPA'S STORY: AN ANGRY KING

GODPAPA'S STORY: THE CRACKATOOK

TIME FOR TEA

VICTORY

THE LAND OF SWEETS

THE CITY

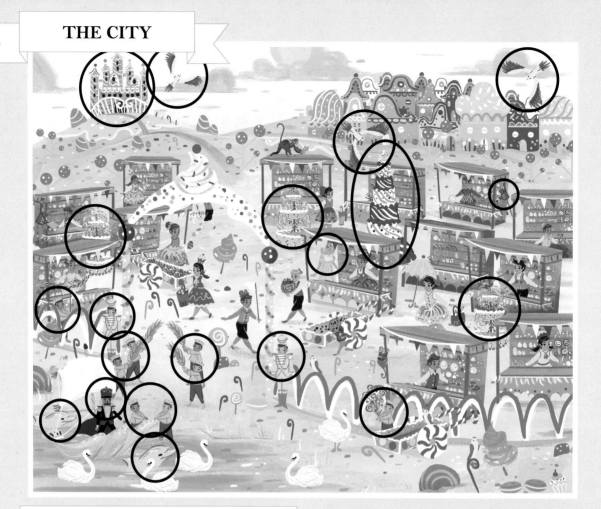

HAPPILY EVER AFTER

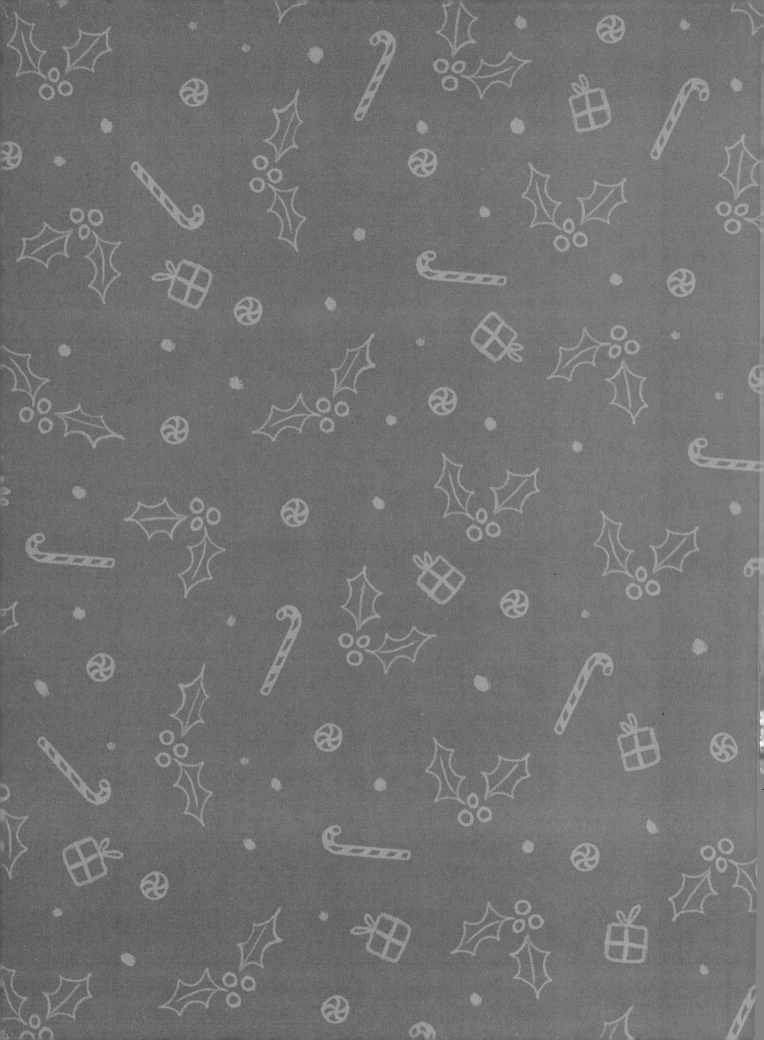